2021

Your Year of Healing

Your hope, peace, and courage companion.

Amit Sood, MD MS FACP

Disclaimer

The information in this book is not intended to substitute a health care
provider's advice or medical care. Please consult your physician or
other health care provider if you are experiencing any symptoms or
have questions pertaining to the information contained in this book.

How to Use this Journal

Your 24-week companion is divided into twelve parts. Each part has a theme and an inspiring person who embodied that theme.

Each day offers you an insight (in italics) and a question or a statement that invites a response. Think and write as you convert this journal into a cherished companion you will treasure for a long time.

Here is an example of a day:

 Day 3

Just as trees grow their branches toward the sun, spend more time with the people who are your source of love and light.

What's special about the people who are the source of love and light in your life?

1. *They are always ready to help.*

2. *They make me laugh.*

3. *They help me feel worthy.*

4. *They treat everyone with kindness.*

5. *They have great energy.*

Through thinking and writing, you'll discover new ways of making small shifts in your life. Small consistent shifts accumulate over a period of time, and open a path of coping, healing, and thriving.

For more information about our online "Year of Healing" initiative, please visit resilientoption.com.

**To all the world's healers.
You are one of them.**

Cope to Heal. Heal to Thrive.

Adversities can leave you unchanged, break you, or inspire you to grow and rise. Breaking is a non-option. While remaining unchanged is okay, a much better option is to grow and rise.

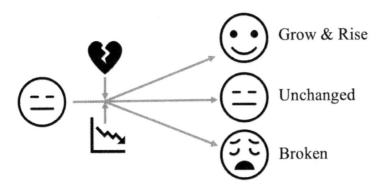

Growing and rising because of adversity occur in three interlocking steps—coping, healing, and thriving.

Coping is taking the challenge head-on. It is adjusting your sail and recruiting all your resources to prevail over the storm.

> ## Coping
>
> Handling a challenge responsibly and effectively.

Healing restores a sense of wholeness by finding a comforting meaning and a connection between your story and that of others. Such meaning doesn't negate suffering but is a reflection of awakening wisdom borne out of the pain.

Healing

Restoring a sense of wholeness.

Thriving naturally emerges from successful coping and healing. When you thrive, you flourish. You achieve possibilities—better physical health, emotional wellbeing, professional success, fulfilling relationships, spiritual upliftment—that would have eluded you, if your entire life was just smooth sailing.

Thriving

Becoming healthy, successful, and strong.

Challenging times can bring out the best in us. Thinking about the people who remained strong despite tremendous personal adversity gives me courage, fills me with hope, and inspires me to keep going. It helps me look at life through a different lens.

Let's look at life with the lens of twelve inspiring people: Helen Keller, Mahatma Gandhi, Marie Curie, Abraham Lincoln, Rosa Parks, Alexander Fleming, Mother Teresa, Martin Luther King Jr., Eleanor Roosevelt, Nelson Mandela, Joan of Arc, and Harriet Tubman. They remind us of the highest places the human minds can go. I hope meditating on the lives of these people might help you stumble onto a deeper meaning, and thus healing.

How will you know that you are healing? You will become kinder. You will feel grateful, despite your struggles. You will realize that an excellent way to heal is to heal someone else. The day we focus less on our aches and more on helping someone else who is hurting, we will start healing, and march toward thriving.

In medicine researchers often say, and it's true, that healing doesn't need a cure. Let's not wait for the cure of all our adversities to begin the process of healing. That will be a very long wait. Let's start the coping-healing-thriving journey today…now.

Each day during 2021, at resilientoption.com, I will post an insight, a suggested practice, and a brief audio recording of the practice I will implement for the day. I will also share it on Twitter at @amitsoodmd. Join me if you have a few minutes!

Your 24-Week Journey

Weeks	Inspiring Figure	Theme
1-2	Helen Keller	Never give up
3-4	Mahatma Gandhi	Have impeccable values, stick to your ideals
5-6	Marie Curie	Give your best, be generous
7-8	Abraham Lincoln	Be kind, have exceptional integrity
9-10	Rosa Parks	Live with dignity and grace
11-12	Alexander Fleming	Be humble, be curious
13-14	Mother Teresa	Serve the underprivileged
15-16	Martin Luther King Jr.	Dream big, chase your dreams
17-18	Eleanor Roosevelt	Live each day with courage and purpose
19-20	Nelson Mandela	Think big, forgive, be patient
21-22	Joan of Arc	Aim high and believe in yourself
23-24	Harriet Tubman	Help those facing the pain you had to endure

Part I (Weeks 1-2)

Theme: Never give up
Inspiring figure: Helen Keller

Imagine losing vision and hearing at 19 months of age and then graduating Phi Beta Kappa, writing 12 books, getting the Presidential Medal of Freedom, and being inducted into the National Women's Hall of Fame. That's what Helen Keller, a true role model of resilience, accomplished. Her life was strongly influenced by Anne Sullivan, Keller's companion, teacher, friend, and her source of light for nearly 50 years, helping Keller overcome her physical limitations.

Here are three of Helen Keller's most inspiring quotes:

"Although the world is full of suffering, it is also full of the overcoming of it."

"The best and most beautiful things in the world cannot be seen or even touched - they must be felt with the heart."

"Alone we can do so little; together we can do so much."

Day 1

Recognize that a lot is still in your control. While you can't stop the snow, you can open the umbrella.

List five things that are still in your control.

1. What I eat
2. How I treat People
3. When I go to bed
4. How I choose to exercise my Body
5. How I Think about life +

    plans & my Body + Goob!

⁓⁓ ⁓ ⁓⁓⁓ ⁓ ⁓⁓

Day 2

Every person is resilient in a unique way. Ask not, if I am resilient; ask, how am I resilient?

Think of your unique strengths and note them here.

1._____

2._____

3._____

4._____

5._____

Day 3

Just as trees grow their branches toward the sun, spend more time with the people who are your source of love and light.

What's special about the people who are the source of love and light in your life?

1._____

2._____

3._____

4._____

5._____

⚘ — ⚘⚘⚘ — ⚘

Day 4

Your heart first serves blood to itself, to serve the body. Be kind to yourself to be kind to others.

Note different ways you can be kind to yourself today.

1._____

2._____

3._____

4._____

5._____

Day 5

Think of what made you happy before you got busy with life. It'll give you an idea of how to be happy again.

Try and recall a few simple things that made you happy as a child.

1._____

2._____

3._____

4._____

5._____

Day 6

Although shoveling doesn't melt the snow, it pushes the snow to the side. Some problems that can't be cured today are best brushed aside, to keep moving forward.

Think of the problems you can push aside for now so you can live your day lifting only the next hour's load.

1._____

2._____

3._____

4._____

5._____

Day 7

Visit your past six days' insights and writings.

Pick out your best ideas and note them here.

1._____

2._____

3._____

4._____

5._____

∞——c∞∞——∞

Day 8

The path to success isn't straight up. If today feels like a step back, consider that it may well be the safest and quickest path to climb higher.

Think of a few ways a recent adversity may have helped you.

1._____

2._____

3._____

4._____

5._____

Day 9

Research shows although we can't change our genetic sequence, we can choose which genes are expressed. And that may be enough.

Think of a few ways you can overcome one of your limitations or take better care of yourself.

1.＿＿＿＿＿＿＿＿＿＿＿＿＿＿＿＿＿＿＿＿＿＿＿

2.＿＿＿＿＿＿＿＿＿＿＿＿＿＿＿＿＿＿＿＿＿＿＿

3.＿＿＿＿＿＿＿＿＿＿＿＿＿＿＿＿＿＿＿＿＿＿＿

4.＿＿＿＿＿＿＿＿＿＿＿＿＿＿＿＿＿＿＿＿＿＿＿

5.＿＿＿＿＿＿＿＿＿＿＿＿＿＿＿＿＿＿＿＿＿＿＿

Day 10

Receiving entails giving and giving entails receiving. Feel grateful for the help you received and the help you were able to give.

List the people who have helped you by agreeing to receive your help.

1.＿＿＿＿＿＿＿＿＿＿＿＿＿＿＿＿＿＿＿＿＿＿＿

2.＿＿＿＿＿＿＿＿＿＿＿＿＿＿＿＿＿＿＿＿＿＿＿

3.＿＿＿＿＿＿＿＿＿＿＿＿＿＿＿＿＿＿＿＿＿＿＿

4.＿＿＿＿＿＿＿＿＿＿＿＿＿＿＿＿＿＿＿＿＿＿＿

5.＿＿＿＿＿＿＿＿＿＿＿＿＿＿＿＿＿＿＿＿＿＿＿

Day 11

Crying helps immunity and is our way of healing. Often, the best laughs come only after the heart is emptied of tears.

Think of a few kind people you know who are easily moved to tears.

1._____

2._____

3._____

4._____

5._____

Day 12

Waiting for a big achievement to feel grateful could be a very long wait. Fill your day with gratitude for the ordinary and simple.

Think of five simple things are you grateful for today.

1._____

2._____

3._____

4._____

5._____

Day 13

Spills happen. Your two best choices are: First clean up and then have a good laugh. Or, first have a good laugh and then clean up!

Which of the past "spills" you're willing to let go today?

1._____

2._____

3._____

4._____

5._____

Day 14

Visit your past six days' writings.

Pick out your best ideas and note them here.

1._____

2._____

3._____

4._____

5._____

Part II (Weeks 3-4)

Theme: Have impeccable values; stick to your ideals
Inspiring figure: Mahatma Gandhi

A modestly successful lawyer, moved by his personal insult and the plight of those around him, launched the most powerful non-violent movement the world has ever seen. His work brought freedom to India and inspired several non-violent and civil rights movements across the globe.

Here are three of Gandhi's most inspiring quotes:

"Be the change that you wish to see in the world."

"Live as if you were to die tomorrow. Learn as if you were to live forever."

"An eye for an eye will only make the whole world blind."

Day 15

Recognize that the people you find annoying often have constraints that you don't know and may never know.

Think of a few good reasons why someone annoying may be justified from within his or her perspective.

1._____

2._____

3._____

4._____

5._____

Day 16

Remembering a good deed is as joyous the tenth time as it is the first time. Seed future happiness by doing something good today.

List five good deeds you have done in the past.

1._____

2._____

3._____

4._____

5._____

Day 17

During a difficult moment, it helps to ask what kind of a story I wish to tell in the future about how I handled this moment.

Think of a few ways you can handle a present difficult situation with grace.

1._____

2._____

3._____

4._____

5._____

Day 18

Do not judge yourself if you were slow and unproductive today. Some days are like that. The important thing is you kept going.

Think of why not every day can be equally productive and it's OK to be non-productive at times.

1._____

2._____

3._____

4._____

5._____

Day 19

Ordinary activity performed with extraordinary presence becomes extraordinary. Consider transforming an ordinary experience today.

Engage with a few simple daily experiences assuming they are extra special.

1._____

2._____

3._____

4._____

5._____

Day 20

A lot may have happened today. How you feel depends on what you ignore and what you look with a magnifying glass.

What are the top five things that went right today?

1._____

2._____

3._____

4._____

5._____

Day 21

Visit your past six days' writings.

Pick out your best ideas and note them here.

1._____

2._____

3._____

4._____

5._____

Day 22

Do not peg your self-worth on your paycheck. Peg your self-worth on the meaning you fulfill and the values you live by.

List the people you are helping through everything you do in your life.

1._____

2._____

3._____

4._____

5._____

Day 23

Best not to multitask when spending time with people; partial presence feels worse than absence.

Commit to giving five-minutes of complete presence to a few people this week.

1._____

2._____

3._____

4._____

5._____

―――――――― ❦ ――――――――

Day 24

Trees don't make roots just on the night of the storm. Build your positivity muscles, little by little, every single day.

Write the core values that guide your personal and professional life.

1._____

2._____

3._____

4._____

5._____

Day 25

Our brain focuses on and believes the criticisms, much more than the compliments. Do not discount the compliments, however small, that come your way.

What are some of the nicest words you have heard about yourself?

1._____

2._____

3._____

4._____

5._____

Day 26

If you have been hurt and can't forgive just yet, keep the intent to forgive. That may be enough to free your mind in this moment.

Write five good things about someone who annoys you.

1._____

2._____

3._____

4._____

5._____

Day 27

Carefully choose the gadgets you allow in your life. Leverage technology to enhance and not replace your presence.

Think of the technology and gadgets you can remove or add to your life to improve your connection with your friends and loved ones.

1._____

2._____

3._____

4._____

5._____

Day 28

Visit your past six days' writings.

Pick out your best ideas and note them here.

1._____

2._____

3._____

4._____

5._____

Part III (Weeks 5-6)

Theme: Give your best, be generous
Inspiring figure: Marie Curie

Growing up with few resources, partly because of her family's patriotic engagements, Marie Curie was the first woman to become a Professor at the University of Paris, and the first person (and woman) to win the Nobel Prize in two fields, Physics and Chemistry. A philanthropist, she donated much of her Nobel Prize money and chose not to patent radium-isolation so others could freely use it.

Here are three of Curie's most inspiring quotes:

"Nothing in life is to be feared. It is only to be understood."

"First principle: never to let one's self be beaten down by persons or by events."

"Radium is not to enrich anyone. It is an element; it is for all people"

Day 29

The meaning that drives you is more powerful than the fears that hold you.

Think of the different ways you are a blessing to this world.

1._____

2._____

3._____

4._____

5._____

Day 30

Birds with asymmetric feathers are the ones that fly. Perhaps, your day's asymmetries, even though annoying, are providing you a lift.

Think of a few daily experiences that are annoying but helpful.

1._____

2._____

3._____

4._____

5._____

Day 31

Our sun boils and freezes many planets before getting it just right. Expect your many efforts will fail before you get it just right.

Recognize all the hard work, sacrifices, and compromises you had to make to be where you are today.

1._____

2._____

3._____

4._____

5._____

Day 32

Hope doesn't mean it won't get dark. Hope means no matter how dark the night, the sun will appear. It always has and always will.

Who and what gives you hope today?

1._____

2._____

3._____

4._____

5._____

Day 33

Not all battles are worth fighting. Carefully choose which battles are worthy of your time and which ones are best bypassed.

Which challenges are you okay with letting go because they aren't worth your time?

1._____

2._____

3._____

4._____

5._____

Day 34

Feel extra gratitude and love for all the animals in your life today. Life's spark is precious in every being.

List the animals in your life and think loving thoughts about them.

1._____

2._____

3._____

4._____

5._____

Day 35

Visit your past six days' writings.

Pick out your best ideas and note them here.

1._____

2._____

3._____

4._____

5._____

Day 36

Now more than ever, nurture a healthier immune system through nourishing diet, moderate exercise, adequate sleep, and connecting with loved ones and friends.

List personal changes you can make for a healthier immune system.

1._____

2._____

3._____

4._____

5._____

Day 37

Older trees provide shade and not fruit, and that's enough. Best to respect and value our seniors. They are the cherished treasures of our family and our world.

Think of how you can help a senior in your life feel valued and loved.

1._____

2._____

3._____

4._____

5._____

Day 38

Seeing the good in the bad isn't denying the bad. It is denying the bad from taking over your mind.

Think of what went right within something that went wrong.

1._____

2._____

3._____

4._____

5._____

Day 39

Adding honey dilutes the bitter in the tea. Similarly, adding gratitude and meaning dilutes life's challenges, making them more bearable.

Try and find gratitude and meaning in a previous life challenge.

1._____

2._____

3._____

4._____

5._____

Day 40

No matter what you do, your job description includes being a happiness officer—at work and at home—for others and yourself.

Think of how you can make others and yourself a little happier today.

1._____

2._____

3._____

4._____

5._____

Day 41

We compare our weaknesses with others' strengths and their weaknesses with our strengths. This creates judgment toward others and self. Every person is strong and weak in his or her unique way.

List some of your strengths that many people don't know.

1._____

2._____

3._____

4._____

5._____

~~~~~~~~~~~~~~~~~~~~~

Day 42

Visit your past six days' writings.

Pick out your best ideas and note them here.

1._____

2._____

3._____

4._____

5._____

Part IV (Weeks 7-8)

Theme: Be kind; have exceptional integrity
Inspiring figure: Abraham Lincoln

With little formal education, Abraham Lincoln self-educated himself to become a successful lawyer, rose to become a U.S. congressman and finally the 16th President of the United States. Two of his most notable contributions were his leadership during the Civil War and his Emancipation Proclamation. He was a humble and kind person, known for his exceptional integrity.

Here are three of Lincoln's most inspiring quotes:

"Whatever you are, be a good one."

"Do I not destroy my enemies when I make them my friends?"

"Give me six hours to chop down a tree and I will spend the first four sharpening the axe."

Day 43

The path to remarkable success is invariably marked with unanticipated hurdles. Many step-backs in reality are move forwards.

Think of how a previous step-back could have been a move forward.

1._____

2._____

3._____

4._____

5._____

❦ ⋅ ❦ ⋅ ❦

Day 44

Smile and say hello. There is a better than one in two chance that the person in front of you feels vulnerable and lonely.

Think of moments during the day you can be a little kinder and more engaged.

1._____

2._____

3._____

4._____

5._____

Day 45

People throwing darts at you likely have an unhealthy relationship with the self. Those unkind to others are often unkind to themselves.

Think of how someone unkind may himself be struggling with low self-worth.

1._____

2._____

3._____

4._____

5._____

Day 46

Just as a scrubber is to dishes, many of our adversaries are to us. They might sound annoying, but in the long term, help us shine.

Appreciate adversaries who challenge you and thus help you grow.

1._____

2._____

3._____

4._____

5._____

Day 47

If all the musical instruments sound identical there would be no orchestra. Appreciate, honor, value, and welcome our differences.

Notice some differences that you value in others.

1._____

2._____

3._____

4._____

5._____

Day 48

The world is a giant tree, and we all are individual leaves on the tree, distinct yet profoundly connected.

Think of a few ways you are connected to others.

1._____

2._____

3._____

4._____

5._____

Day 49

Visit your past six days' writings.

Pick out your best ideas and note them here.

1._____

2._____

3._____

4._____

5._____

— ❧ ❧ ❧ —

Day 50

With the world full of so much pain, seeking happiness just for the self might provoke guilt. The best way to find happiness is to stumble on it while seeking hope and healing for others.

Think of ways you can help one person feel a little more hopeful today.

1._____

2._____

3._____

4._____

5._____

Day 51

A farmer feeds the nation, a teacher educates the nation, a hospital janitor saves lives. Align your work with the deepest purpose—to better negotiate the annoying and the stressful.

Think of the deeper purpose of yours and others' work.

1._____

2._____

3._____

4._____

5._____

Day 52

Today, if we are privileged to be grateful, then we have a responsibility to be compassionate.

Think of a few ways you can share your blessings with others.

1._____

2._____

3._____

4._____

5._____

Day 53

Authenticity is more important than positivity. Feeling emotions that are congruent with your reality is more helpful than forcing happiness.

Think of a few reasons why negative emotions can be helpful.

1._____

2._____

3._____

4._____

5._____

Day 54

Just as in the cold lifeless space, our planet thrives in its bubble of air (our atmosphere), you may have to create your own bubble of positivity, if the world around gets cold or chaotic.

Think of perspectives you can use to remain positive even during difficult times.

1._____

2._____

3._____

4._____

5._____

Day 55

It is nearly impossible to feel bad about yourself during moments you are wishing others well. Wish others well to enhance your self-worth.

Send a silent good wish to at least five people today. Make sure you include one or more people who mildly annoy you in that list.

1._____

2._____

3._____

4._____

5._____

Day 56

Visit your past six days' writings.

Pick out your best ideas and note them here.

1._____

2._____

3._____

4._____

5._____

Part V (Weeks 9-10)

Theme: Live with dignity and grace
Inspiring figure: Rosa Parks

Famously called "the first lady of civil rights," Rosa Parks grew in a segregated world that she resented. Her refusal to give up her seat was the culmination of decades of her learning in defiance and equality. The resulting arrest and her "quiet strength" sparked a drive that made segregation unconstitutional and launched the Civil Rights Movement.

Here are three of Park's most inspiring quotes:

"You must never be fearful about what you are doing when it is right."

"The only tired I was, was tired of giving in."

"No."

Day 57

When you say No, you aren't being unkind. You are being kind to yourself.

Add one or more items to your Not-To-Do list today—something you choose not to do because it doesn't enrich your life.

1._____

2._____

3._____

4._____

5._____

Day 58

Research shows courageous people don't have less fear. They choose to keep going despite the fear.

What are some compelling reasons for you to keep going?

1._____

2._____

3._____

4._____

5._____

Day 59

Go back to your earliest memories and spend a few minutes thinking about the people who helped you feel worthy and loved.

Who all have helped you the most in your life's struggles?

1._____

2._____

3._____

4._____

5._____

Day 60

Worries deplete your today without nourishing your tomorrow. You can't rid yourself of all the worries, but you can choose to dilute them with hope, courage, and faith.

What are some of the most courageous things you have done?

1._____

2._____

3._____

4._____

5._____

Day 61

Our barrier to compassion isn't the absence of it; it is limiting our compassion to a select few who we believe deserve our compassion.

Think of expanding your compassion to a few people or groups of people you may have judged in the past.

1._____

2._____

3._____

4._____

5._____

Day 62

Excessive fear makes us irrational and irrationality increases fear. Let your fears keep you safe and not paralyze you into inaction.

What are some unhelpful irrational fears that you are willing to shed?

1._____

2._____

3._____

4._____

5._____

Day 63

Visit your past six days' writings.

Pick out your best ideas and note them here.

1._____

2._____

3._____

4._____

5._____

Day 64

We all are profoundly similar to each other; much more than we are different. Discovering similarities helps us become kinder.

Think of a few similarities between you and someone you find annoying.

1._____

2._____

3._____

4._____

5._____

Day 65

Sometimes, it helps to notice a neighborhood yard with more weeds, to enjoy yours with fewer.

Think of a few ways you have been uniquely blessed.

1._____

2._____

3._____

4._____

5._____

Day 66

Trees can teach you selflessness, dogs-love, toddlers-curiosity, weeds-hardiness, dolphins-play. Pick your teacher for today.

Think of the life lessons you can learn from the nature and animals.

1._____

2._____

3._____

4._____

5._____

Day 67

"What's the ultimate meaning of life?" is a difficult question. A better question is: How can I make my life more meaningful?

Think of a few ways you can add more meaning to your days.

1._____

2._____

3._____

4._____

5._____

Day 68

The dominating and the dominated both live in fear. Joy and fulfillment are in feeling equal and helping others feel equal.

Think of how no one is superior or inferior. We are all equal.

1._____

2._____

3._____

4._____

5._____

Day 69

Many stuff toys look prettier and more perfect than original. If it was just about beauty and perfection, we would be living with stuff-toy partners.

What are some of the most profound qualities in your partner/friend?

1._____

2._____

3._____

4._____

5._____

Day 70

Visit your past six days' writings.

Pick out your best ideas and note them here.

1._____

2._____

3._____

4._____

5._____

Part VI (Weeks 11-12)

Theme: Be humble, be curious
Inspiring figure: Alexander Fleming

Not many can claim that their work has saved over a hundred million lives. One of them was the humble Alexander Fleming. His curiosity and brilliance found a hidden antibiotic (Penicillin) in a petri dish that was accidentally left open and grew mold that inhibited the surrounding bacteria. Penicillin has influenced advances in almost every medical field, including surgery and organ transplants.

Here are three of Fleming's most inspiring quotes:

"The unprepared mind cannot see the outstretched hand of opportunity."

"My only merit is that I did not neglect the observation."

"Nature makes penicillin; I just found it."

Day 71

It helps to consider an unplanned detour an adventure. Such an outlook saves you energy to find your path back to the highway.

Do you know of instances when an annoying delay or a mistake turned out to be eventually helpful?

1._____

2._____

3._____

4._____

5._____

Day 72

In the sky today you can see the same dull clouds, or a formation never seen before. Every "boring day" offers you the same choice.

Think of how the simplest of experiences can be deeply precious.

1._____

2._____

3._____

4._____

5._____

Day 73

Success is preceded and followed by failure. If you're successful, rest assured you'll fail; if you're failing, rest assured you'll succeed.

Think of how a previous failure may have seeded today's success.

1._____

2._____

3._____

4._____

5._____

Day 74

Humility isn't low self-worth. Humility knows that you are worthy, just as others are. Humility accepts praise where due and is generous in praising others.

What are some reasons you like to spend time with the humble people?

1._____

2._____

3._____

4._____

5._____

Day 75

Your patience is your treat to others and yourself. When you gift them your patience, you gift them and yourself peace and happiness.

Think of times during the day when you could be more patient.

1._____

2._____

3._____

4._____

5._____

Day 76

Notice for a few seconds the color of your loved one's eyes. This little practice can boost your oxytocin (the bonding hormone) and fill you with joy.

Can you recall the color of the eyes of a few of your friends and loved ones?

1._____

2._____

3._____

4._____

5._____

Day 77

Visit your past six days' writings.

Pick out your best ideas and note them here.

1._____

2._____

3._____

4._____

5._____

Day 78

A novel object or person draws attention. Interestingly, when we start paying attention, what seemed ordinary starts looking novel.

Find new (interesting) details in a few simple things around you.

1._____

2._____

3._____

4._____

5._____

Day 79

I was much wiser in kindergarten. I knew sharing. I knew how to laugh, hug, love. I could forget myself for hours.

What are some of the most admirable qualities in a kindergartener?

1._____

2._____

3._____

4._____

5._____

Day 80

Who can be more selfless than a tree that produces seedless fruits? Act like a tree today, sharing your gifts with no expectations of a reward.

Think of ways you can live a more selfless day today.

1._____

2._____

3._____

4._____

5._____

Day 81

Appreciate what seems easy. It is easy today because someone spent years simplifying what was then difficult or near impossible.

What are some of today's daily conveniences that weren't available to us a hundred years ago?

1._____

2._____

3._____

4._____

5._____

Day 82

See a dad or mom in a cab driver, a son or daughter in the mail person. Look at others from within their circle of love.

Think of why the people you meet every day are more precious than many of us generally believe.

1._____

2._____

3._____

4._____

5._____

Day 83

We can't inhale without exhaling or exhale without inhaling. Similarly, we can't give without receiving or receive without giving. It's a circle.

Think of the many ways you can be grateful for the help you were able to give.

1._____

2._____

3._____

4._____

5._____

Day 84

Visit your past six days' writings.

Pick out your best ideas and note them here.

1._____

2._____

3._____

4._____

5._____

Part VII (Weeks 13-14)

Theme: Serve the underprivileged
Inspiring figure: Mother Teresa

"Never eat a single mouthful unless you are sharing it with others."
That's what Agnes learned from her mother. She became Mother
Teresa, having taken the vow of poverty, chastity, and obedience. A
Nobel laureate, her Order of the Missionaries of Charity,
orphanages, foundations, and hospices serve millions of poor and
needy. She was canonized a Saint in 2016.

Here are three of Saint Teresa's most inspiring quotes:

"If you judge people, you have no time to love them."

*"Not all of us can do great things. But we can do small things with
great love."*

*"If we have no peace, it is because we have forgotten that we belong
to each other."*

Day 85

When brewing happiness and love for others, you can't help but first taste it yourself.

Think of a few ways you can help others feel worthy and loved.

1._____

2._____

3._____

4._____

5._____

———— ⌘ ————

Day 86

Assume you are a role model for thousands of children. Live your day modeling the right behavior for these children.

Think of what you would do differently if you knew that thousands of children were looking up to you as their role model.

1._____

2._____

3._____

4._____

5._____

Day 87

Replace the word work in your dictionary with service, purpose, and prayer.

Think how your work is bringing hope, help, and healing to at least one person in the world.

1._____

2._____

3._____

4._____

5._____

Day 88

If you feel you are lost on the dirt roads today, remember that all small roads eventually meet a highway.

Think of the different ways you are connected to the world.

1._____

2._____

3._____

4._____

5._____

Day 89

Compassion isn't just diluting sorrow; it is also multiplying joy. When you are truly, deeply happy for others in their happy moments, you are being compassionate.

Find creative ways of participating in others' happy moments.

1._____

2._____

3._____

4._____

5._____

Day 90

Just as you decorate your face with the right make up in the morning, decorate your mind with gratitude and kindness before you start your day.

Think a few kind and grateful thoughts in this moment.

1._____

2._____

3._____

4._____

5._____

Day 91

Visit your past six days' writings.

Pick out your best ideas and note them here.

1._____

2._____

3._____

4._____

5._____

Day 92

Not every pain can be explained by an abnormal MRI scan. Help those struggling feel validated and cared, not judged and belittled.

Think of how we can stop judging and start validating (at least in our own mind) others who are hurting.

1._____

2._____

3._____

4._____

5._____

Day 93

Send success to the heart (so you are kinder) and failure to the head (so you are wiser).

What inspirations can you learn from the people who are humble and kind in success, and take failure in stride?

1._____

2._____

3._____

4._____

5._____

———— ⚜ ————

Day 94

The people and the principles you serve are your main source of strength. No one living a life of service says at the end of it—"I should have been a little more selfish."

Think of how serving others has made you stronger.

1._____

2._____

3._____

4._____

5._____

Day 95

Pick the title of your biography—suffering or overcoming. The chapters that fill the book will follow.

Think of how you embodied strength in your previous struggles.

1._____

2._____

3._____

4._____

5._____

Day 96

Grace is like the sunlight, but it is up to us to open the blinds. Close your blinds when the world gets dark, but let the light in, when the day seems bright and inviting.

Think of the many ways you are blessed today.

1._____

2._____

3._____

4._____

5._____

Day 97

*Joy is in caring. The day we start treating rental cars as our own,
will be the day we will know how to be joyous.*

Think of how you can be extra gentle with the things you own today.

1._____

2._____

3._____

4._____

5._____

Day 98

Visit your past six days' writings.

Pick out your best ideas and note them here.

1._____

2._____

3._____

4._____

5._____

Part VIII (Weeks 15-16)

Theme: Dream big; chase your dreams
Inspiring figure: Martin Luther King Jr.

Learning from his father that segregation and racism are an affront to God's will, MLK Jr. grew with the values of dignity and respect. He organized the Southern Christian Leadership Conference, led the Civil Rights Movement, pursued non-violent activism, and was instrumental in the Civil Rights and Voting Act and ending segregation. He received the Nobel Peace Prize in 1964 at age 35.

Here are three of MLK Jr.'s most inspiring quotes:

"Our lives begin to end the day we become silent about things that matter."

"Darkness cannot drive out darkness: only light can do that. Hate cannot drive out hate: only love can do that."

"Injustice anywhere is a threat to justice everywhere."

Day 99

People who stand strong despite all the rough and tumble give us courage. Keep such people in your thoughts.

Think of the good qualities of one or more resilient people who fill you with hope and courage.

1._____

2._____

3._____

4._____

5._____

Day 100

The more fruits on a branch the more it bends. Your humility is a sign of your true accomplishments.

Think of how humility can help you become emotionally stronger.

1._____

2._____

3._____

4._____

5._____

Day 101

*When one hand is relieved of pain, the entire body feels the comfort.
Our compassionate spirit shares each other's pain and healing.*

Think of how you can connect with and help someone who may be
hurting.

1._____

2._____

3._____

4._____

5._____

Day 102

*If you are struggling with forgiveness, start with forgiving the self.
Forgiving others often starts with forgiving the self.*

Think of how despite good intentions mistakes can happen and
forgiveness makes sense.

1._____

2._____

3._____

4._____

5._____

Day 103

Engage people's heart not their defenses, particularly with the children and the vulnerable. Validate and love, to teach and inspire.

Think of how you can validate and express love toward children and the vulnerable people you know.

1._____

2._____

3._____

4._____

5._____

Day 104

While we run on different tracks, we all are united by our shared past and future. I, you, and they all belong to our common single ancestry tree.

Find different ways you are connected to others.

1._____

2._____

3._____

4._____

5._____

Day 105

Visit your past six days' writings.

Pick out your best ideas and note them here.

1._____

2._____

3._____

4._____

5._____

Day 106

Deep within you is a song that has lyrics of hope and courage, and music of joy and love. Sing that song today; yours is as melodious as any.

Think of why it makes sense to go ahead and sing your song instead of spending too much time judging the quality of your voice?

1._____

2._____

3._____

4._____

5._____

Day 107

The antidotes to fear are logic, action, acceptance, meaning, connection, and faith. Make your own recipe by picking the ideas and principles that make the most sense to you.

Think of the different ways you can better manage your fears.

1._____

2._____

3._____

4._____

5._____

Day 108

Anger can be helpful when it becomes a force of reason that puts energy into peaceful efforts to decrease suffering.

Think of the different ways you can better manage your anger.

1._____

2._____

3._____

4._____

5._____

Day 109

More than fame and fortune, I pray your children feel loved in the world and are skilled at loving themselves.

Write your hopes for your and all the worlds' children.

1._____

2._____

3._____

4._____

5._____

Day 110

The day we start living to please the sacred within us, will be the day we'll stop thinking, saying, or doing anything regrettable and hurtful.

Think of a few reasons you are truly priceless.

1._____

2._____

3._____

4._____

5._____

Day 111

You're more likely to win when you play for the home team. No matter where you work, try to selflessly help the world, to secure more wins.

Think of how you are working for the whole world, and the whole world is your home.

1._____

2._____

3._____

4._____

5._____

Day 112

Visit your past six days' writings.

Pick out your best ideas and note them here.

1._____

2._____

3._____

4._____

5._____

Part IX (Weeks 17-18)

Theme: Live each day with courage and purpose
Inspiring figure: Eleanor Roosevelt

Eleanor Roosevelt wasn't going to be just a symbol of elegance as the first lady. She ran her own press briefings (with only female reporters), took an active part in politics, and became "the President's eyes, ears, and legs." She advocated for the disadvantaged, became the first chair of the UN Commission on Human Rights, and indeed became, "the first lady of the world."

Here are three of ER's most inspiring quotes:

"Do what you feel in your heart to be right – for you'll be criticized anyway."

"No one can make you feel inferior without your consent."

"It isn't enough to talk about peace. One must believe in it. And it isn't enough to believe in it. One must work at it."

Day 113

Courage isn't the lack of fear. Courage is going forward and doing the right thing despite the fear.

Think of who and what gives you the most courage.

1._____

2._____

3._____

4._____

5._____

Day 114

Four nourishments for the mind: meaningful work, time with loved ones, nature walk, and faith. Pick your selection/s for today!

Think of the different ways you can nourish your mind today.

1._____

2._____

3._____

4._____

5._____

Day 115

It is impossible for two passionate intelligent people to live in the same space and always agree.

Think of a few aspects in which you and someone close to you can peacefully disagree.

1._____

2._____

3._____

4._____

5._____

Day 116

Meet people as a jet bridge meets the aircraft—with gentleness, purpose, and grace. Together, you will fulfill a greater meaning.

Plan how you will be extra gentle to the people you'll be meeting today.

1._____

2._____

3._____

4._____

5._____

Day 117

Use your present wisdom to heal and not judge your past. You didn't know then what you know today.

Think of some of the most important things you have learned in life.

1._____

2._____

3._____

4._____

5._____

Day 118

Meet the grownup hiding in your children and the child hiding in the grownups.

Recall (with fondness) examples of maturity in the children and displays of innocence in the grownups in your life.

1._____

2._____

3._____

4._____

5._____

Day 119

Visit your past six days' writings.

Pick out your best ideas and note them here.

1._____

2._____

3._____

4._____

5._____

Day 120

The past is easier to change than the future. You can change your past by assigning it a different meaning.

Think differently about your past, with a focus on finding a meaning that provides healing.

1._____

2._____

3._____

4._____

5._____

Day 121

Assume today that every blessing is healing you, every loving gesture is touching you, every child is your child, you'll never be alone.

Look at your life and think about the experiences and people who soothe your mind and provide you healing.

1._____

2._____

3._____

4._____

5._____

Day 122

Let's do our part in creating a world where no hurt is left unhealed and no one is intentionally hurt. Today is a great day to start.

Think about how you can bring healing to your world.

1._____

2._____

3._____

4._____

5._____

Day 123

If removing someone from your heart is too painful, then move that person to a different chamber of the heart—from the chamber that hosts a loved one or close friend to one that houses an acquaintance or associate.

Think of how you can redefine a relationship to maintain it.

1._____

2._____

3._____

4._____

5._____

Day 124

As you read these words 30,000 people in the world are thinking of taking their life. Feel grateful and compassionate in honor of those who can't access these feelings today.

Think of a few good reasons to be compassionate today.

1._____

2._____

3._____

4._____

5._____

Day 125

Forces that hurt our heart are stronger than ones that break our bone. A tree that resists 70 mph winds can fall to wood beetles that hollow it from inside.

What are different ways you can become stronger from inside?

1._____

2._____

3._____

4._____

5._____

Day 126

Visit your past six days' writings.

Pick out your best ideas and note them here.

1._____

2._____

3._____

4._____

5._____

Part X (Weeks 19-20)

Theme: Think big, forgive, be patient
Inspiring figure: Nelson Mandela

As a young man, Nelson Mandela was profoundly touched by the despair he saw in the eyes of the South African youth. Through diplomacy and non-violent activism, he secured freedom for his country at tremendous personal cost, including jail time for 27 years. One of his most significant contributions was his commitment to forgiveness. No wonder he dropped early his first name, Rolihlala, which means "troublemaker" in the Xhosa language!

Here are three of Mandela's most inspiring quotes:

"Do not judge me by my successes, judge me by how many times I fell down and got back up again."

"May your choices reflect your hopes, not your fears."

"If you talk to a man in a language he understands, that goes to his head. If you talk to him in his language, that goes to his heart."

Day 127

One of the best ways to prepare for forgiveness is to think about those who were hurt worse than you but still chose to forgive.

What can you learn from the kindest most forgiving people you know who have themselves experienced a lot of difficulties?

1._____

2._____

3._____

4._____

5._____

Day 128

If you fall, choose to rise higher than where you fell from. Often, the only time we get to rise is when we have fallen.

Recall instances where you rose because you fell.

1._____

2._____

3._____

4._____

5._____

Day 129

Trying to prove that you are right may be a wasted effort. Much better use of your energy is to prove that you are kind.

Think of how you can show kindness in words and actions.

1._____

2._____

3._____

4._____

5._____

Day 130

Let go of judging someone today who is very sensitive and easily gets hurt. He may be stuck in a difficult situation that he can't tell.

Think of why someone who seems unreasonable may be struggling.

1._____

2._____

3._____

4._____

5._____

Day 131

Practicing patience improves your mood, decreases your risk of accidents, heart disease, and early death, and increases career success. Try to be 10% more patient today.

Think of the people who get you most impatient. Can you commit to greater patience with them today? If yes, how do you plan to do that?

1._____

2._____

3._____

4._____

5._____

Day 132

Let your personal pain help you become compassionate toward others' pain. Suffering that inspires kindness is a force of transformation.

Think of ways you can help others overcome the struggles you had to endure in the past.

1._____

2._____

3._____

4._____

5._____

Day 133

Visit your past six days' writings.

Pick out your best ideas and note them here.

1._____

2._____

3._____

4._____

5._____

Day 134

The better your binoculars, the more scars you see on the moon. The closer you get to know someone, the more flaws you start finding in them.

Think of ways you can lower your expectations of someone close to you.

1._____

2._____

3._____

4._____

5._____

Day 135

We are kinder toward those we find similar to us. Finding similarities warms up our feelings toward each other.

Find similarities with someone who annoys you, to soften your feelings toward that person.

1._____

2._____

3._____

4._____

5._____

Day 136

Four ideas for today—savor your food 10% more, walk 10% more, meet loved ones and friends with 10% more energy, and keep 10% more hope.

Think of what you want to do 10% more today.

1._____

2._____

3._____

4._____

5._____

Day 137

We swim in an ocean of uncertainty. Just as fish can't afford to be afraid of water, we can't afford to be fearful of uncertainty.

Think of one or more uncertainties that you are comfortable accepting for today.

1._____

2._____

3._____

4._____

5._____

Day 138

Sometimes the best of people, despite all the hard work, experience failure. Measure yourself not by your success, but by the values you embody.

Think of the most important values that guide your life.

1._____

2._____

3._____

4._____

5._____

Day 139

A hospital janitor saves as many lives as a doctor. Honor the meaning (how one serves the world), not just the means (what one does).

Think of the profound importance of the work of some people whose contribution is underappreciated.

1._____

2._____

3._____

4._____

5._____

Day 140

Visit your past six days' writings.

Pick out your best ideas and note them here.

1._____

2._____

3._____

4._____

5._____

Part XI (Weeks 21-22)

Theme: Aim high and believe in yourself
Inspiring figure: Joan of Arc

A humble warrior, steadfast in her resolve and guided by divine visions, Joan of Arc, at 16-years of age, launched her mission to free France from foreign forces. She completed that mission at age 17. Not receiving the support that she deserved, she left the planet too soon—as a teenager. Much later, she was canonized and is the patron saint of France.

Here are three of Joan of Arc's most inspiring quotes:

"I am not afraid... I was born to do this."

"Act, and God will act."

"One life is all we have and we live it as we believe in living it. But to sacrifice what you are and to live without belief, that is a fate more terrible than dying."

Day 141

Seek not a life free of adversity. That wish won't be granted. Seek a life of strength to face, fight, and overcome the adversity, and wisdom to grow because of it.

Think of a few examples from your life where a short-term adversity made you stronger and helped you in the long term.

1._____

2._____

3._____

4._____

5._____

Day 142

Remember a past selfless action of yours and try to do something similar to that action.

Think of one or more ways you can be extra altruistic today.

1._____

2._____

3._____

4._____

5._____

Day 143

Personal hurts multiply when you revisit them too often; personal hurts heal when you attend to others who are hurting.

Think of how you can personally heal by helping someone else who is hurting.

1._____

2._____

3._____

4._____

5._____

Day 144

Most people struggle with self-worth and self-doubt. One of the most precious gifts you can give to others is to help them believe in themselves.

Think of ways you can help others feel worthy and confident.

1._____

2._____

3._____

4._____

5._____

Day 145

Love shines the brightest in the hearts purified by wisdom borne of suffering. Let your struggles purify and not demoralize you.

Think of ways you can rise, because you fell.

1._____

2._____

3._____

4._____

5._____

Day 146

Help yourself by helping someone who has no ability to repay you back. That's how we all were lifted one day.

Think of how you can help someone who has no ability to reciprocate.

1._____

2._____

3._____

4._____

5._____

Day 147

Visit your past six days' writings.

Pick out your best ideas and note them here.

1._____

2._____

3._____

4._____

5._____

Day 148

Try your best not to quit. But if you feel spent, nothing wrong with taking a break.

Think of the benefits of intentionally adding a few slow moments to your day.

1._____

2._____

3._____

4._____

5._____

Day 149

Recognize that majority of suffering in the world is invisible. This recognition might help you default to kindness.

Think of a few ways someone who looks strong may be struggling.

1._____

2._____

3._____

4._____

5._____

Day 150

It's easy to be kind to the influential and important people. True kindness is being kind to those who depend on you.

What are the different ways you can be kind to someone who depends on you?

1._____

2._____

3._____

4._____

5._____

Day 151

Empty the space in your brain taken by self-doubt. Replace it with hope, inspiration, and courage.

Think of a few ways you can be more hopeful, inspired, and courageous today.

1._____

2._____

3._____

4._____

5._____

Day 152

Replace fear with hope. Support hope with courage. Direct courage toward meaning.

Think of ways hope and courage can help you fulfill a greater meaning.

1._____

2._____

3._____

4._____

5._____

Day 153

The light is one, the candles many. More the candles, brighter the light.

Think of how others (who you may find "different") are a source of love and light in the world.

1._____

2._____

3._____

4._____

5._____

⊰———∞———⊱

Day 154

Visit your past six days' writings.

Pick out your best ideas and note them here.

1._____

2._____

3._____

4._____

5._____

Part XII (Weeks 23-24)

Theme: Help those facing the pain you had to endure
Inspiring figure: Harriet Tubman

Harriet spent most of her childhood in hardships, enduring emotional and physical abuse. In 1849, after she escaped from slavery, Tubman organized an "underground railroad" that freed over three hundred slaves. No wonder she was called the "Moses." She even led an armed expedition that freed over 700 slaves. After the end of the Civil War, she spent the rest of her life helping former slaves and the elderly.

Here are two of Tubman's most inspiring quotes:

"Every great dream begins with a dreamer. Always remember, you have within you the strength, the patience, and the passion to reach for the stars to change the world."

"I had reasoned this out in my mind; there was one of two things I had a right to, liberty or death; if I could not have one, I would have the other; for no man should take me alive."

Day 155

Showing that you care can reverse the effect of stress on people's brain. You can't lift their load, but your care can help them find greater strength.

Think of how you can help someone who might be struggling today.

1._____

2._____

3._____

4._____

5._____

❧ ⬥ ─── ❦❀❦ ─── ⬥ ❧

Day 156

You only truly receive and experience the love you believe you deserve.

What are the some of the compliments you have received that you fully deserved?

1._____

2._____

3._____

4._____

5._____

The good people in your life are happy in your happiness; you can talk to them at 2 a.m. to share a worry.

Who are the people you can call at 2 a.m. to share a personal concern? Consider connecting with one of them today.

1._____

2._____

3._____

4._____

5._____

 Day 158

You can't fail if you gave a good-faith effort. Success is mostly about trying, and not as much about winning.

How can it help to count your success by your efforts and intentions and not wait for the outcome?

1._____

2._____

3._____

4._____

5._____

Day 159

Let go of the uncontrollable. Focus most of your energy on problems that are important, actionable, and time sensitive.

What are some undesirable but uncontrollable aspects of life you are willing to accept for today?

1._____

2._____

3._____

4._____

5._____

Day 160

When you get busy helping the world, the world gets busy helping you. The world, however, is almost always slower than desired.

Think of instances you are willing to forgive where your good actions were neither recognized nor reciprocated.

1._____

2._____

3._____

4._____

5._____

Day 161

Visit your past six days' writings.

Pick out your best ideas and note them here.

1._____

2._____

3._____

4._____

5._____

Day 162

Research shows living your days with a strong sense of purpose can decrease the risk of heart attack by as much as 25 percent.

What are the different ways you can live your day with a strong sense of purpose?

1._____

2._____

3._____

4._____

5._____

Day 163

The commonest cause of heart failure isn't the heart's inability to squeeze; it is its inability to relax.

What are the different ways you can feel more relaxed today?

1._____

2._____

3._____

4._____

5._____

Day 164

The good people are very good at feeling bad about themselves. If you have felt bad about yourself, it's a proof that you are a good person.

Write a few reasons you are a good person.

1._____

2._____

3._____

4._____

5._____

Day 165

Courage keeps the company of humility. You'll often hear the courageous say, "I was just doing my job."

Who are the most courageous people you know and what gives them their strength?

1._____

2._____

3._____

4._____

5._____

Day 166

Your genes are important, but they aren't your destiny. A more powerful influencer of your future is your strong will guided by your wisdom.

Write a few lessons you have learned in this life.

1._____

2._____

3._____

4._____

5._____

Day 167

When the present moment is challenged, zoom out. When the long term is challenged, zoom in.

Think of a few good things in this moment and a few good things you look forward to in the coming months and years.

1._____

2._____

3._____

4._____

5._____

Day 168

Visit your past six days' writings.

Pick out your best ideas and note them here.

1._____

2._____

3._____

4._____

5._____

Additional Resources by Dr. Sood

Websites: resilientoption.com
immuneresilience.com
happigenius.com

Books: SMART with Dr. Sood
Mayo Clinic Guide to Stress-Free Living
Mayo Clinic Handbook for Happiness
The Resilience Journal
Stronger: The Science and Art of Stress Resilience
Mindfulness Redesigned for the 21st Century

Mobile Apps: Zizo: Your Personal Resilience Assistant
Mood Candy